Glencoe Science

Chapter Resources

Our Impact on Land

Includes:

Reproducible Student Pages

ASSESSMENT

✔ Chapter Tests

✔ Chapter Review

HANDS-ON ACTIVITIES

✔ Lab Worksheets for each Student Edition Activity

✔ Laboratory Activities

✔ Foldables—Reading and Study Skills activity sheet

MEETING INDIVIDUAL NEEDS

✔ Directed Reading for Content Mastery

✔ Directed Reading for Content Mastery in Spanish

✔ Reinforcement

✔ Enrichment

✔ Note-taking Worksheets

TRANSPARENCY ACTIVITIES

✔ Section Focus Transparency Activities

✔ Teaching Transparency Activity

✔ Assessment Transparency Activity

Teacher Support and Planning

✔ Content Outline for Teaching

✔ Spanish Resources

✔ Teacher Guide and Answers

McGraw Hill Glencoe

New York, New York   Columbus, Ohio   Chicago, Illinois   Peoria, Illinois   Woodland Hills, California

Glencoe Science

Photo Credits
Section Focus Transparency 1: Jeff Greenberg/Visuals Unlimited;
Section Focus Transparency 2: (t,inset) Gerry Ellis/ ENP, Inc., (b) Allen Zak Photography;
Section Focus Transparency 3: Courtesy Dr.Greg McPherson, USDA Forest Service,
Dept. of Environmental Horticulture, University of CA, Davis

The McGraw-Hill Companies

Send all inquiries to:
Glencoe/McGraw-Hill
8787 Orion Place
Columbus, OH 43240-4027

ISBN 0-07-866957-X

Printed in the United States of America.

4 5 6 7 8 9 10   009   09 08 07

Table of Contents

Additional Assessment Resources available with Glencoe Science:

- Exam*View*® Pro Testmaker
- Assessment Transparencies
- Performance Assessment in the Science Classroom
- Standardized Test Practice Booklet
- MindJogger Videoquizzes
- Vocabulary PuzzleMaker at **msscience.com**
- Interactive Chalkboard
- The Glencoe Science Web site at: **msscience.com**
- An interactive version of this textbook along with assessment resources are available online at: **mhln.com**

To the Teacher

This chapter-based booklet contains all of the resource materials to help you teach this chapter more effectively. Within you will find:

Reproducible pages for
- Student Assessment
- Hands-on Activities
- Meeting Individual Needs (Extension and Intervention)
- Transparency Activities

A teacher support and planning section including
- Content Outline of the chapter
- Spanish Resources
- Answers and teacher notes for the worksheets

Hands-On Activities

MiniLAB and Lab Worksheets: Each of these worksheets is an expanded version of each lab and MiniLAB found in the Student Edition. The materials lists, procedures, and questions are repeated so that students do not need their texts open during the lab. Write-on rules are included for any questions. Tables/charts/graphs are often included for students to record their observations. Additional lab preparation information is provided in the *Teacher Guide and Answers* section.

Laboratory Activities: These activities do not require elaborate supplies or extensive pre-lab preparations. These student-oriented labs are designed to explore science through a stimulating yet simple and relaxed approach to each topic. Helpful comments, suggestions, and answers to all questions are provided in the *Teacher Guide and Answers* section.

Foldables: At the beginning of each chapter there is a *Foldables: Reading & Study Skills* activity written by renowned educator, Dinah Zike, that provides students with a tool that they can make themselves to organize some of the information in the chapter. Students may make an organizational study fold, a cause and effect study fold, or a compare and contrast study fold, to name a few. The accompanying *Foldables* worksheet found in this resource booklet provides an additional resource to help students demonstrate their grasp of the concepts. The worksheet may contain titles, subtitles, text, or graphics students need to complete the study fold.

Meeting Individual Needs (Extension and Intervention)

Directed Reading for Content Mastery: These worksheets are designed to provide students with learning difficulties with an aid to learning and understanding the vocabulary and major concepts of each chapter. The *Content Mastery* worksheets contain a variety of formats to engage students as they master the basics of the chapter. Answers are provided in the *Teacher Guide and Answers* section.

Directed Reading for Content Mastery (in Spanish): A Spanish version of the *Directed Reading for Content Mastery* is provided for those Spanish-speaking students who are learning English.

Reinforcement: These worksheets provide an additional resource for reviewing the concepts of the chapter. There is one worksheet for each section, or lesson, of the chapter. The *Reinforcement* worksheets are designed to focus primarily on science content and less on vocabulary, although knowledge of the section vocabulary supports understanding of the content. The worksheets are designed for the full range of students; however, they will be more challenging for your lower-ability students. Answers are provided in the *Teacher Guide and Answers* section.

Enrichment: These worksheets are directed toward above-average students and allow them to explore further the information and concepts introduced in the section. A variety of formats are used for these worksheets: readings to analyze; problems to solve; diagrams to examine and analyze; or a simple activity or lab which students can complete in the classroom or at home. Answers are provided in the *Teacher Guide and Answers* section.

Note-taking Worksheet: The *Note-taking Worksheet* mirrors the content contained in the teacher version—*Content Outline for Teaching*. They can be used to allow students to take notes during class, as an additional review of the material in the chapter, or as study notes for students who have been absent.

Assessment

Chapter Review: These worksheets prepare students for the chapter test. The *Chapter Review* worksheets cover all major vocabulary, concepts, and objectives of the chapter. The first part is a vocabulary review and the second part is a concept review. Answers and objective correlations are provided in the *Teacher Guide and Answers* section.

Chapter Test: The *Chapter Test* requires students to use process skills and understand content. Although all questions involve memory to some degree, you will find that your students will need to discover relationships among facts and concepts in some questions, and to use higher levels of critical thinking to apply concepts in other questions. Each chapter test normally consists of four parts: Testing Concepts measures recall and recognition of vocabulary and facts in the chapter; Understanding Concepts requires interpreting information and more comprehension than recognition and recall—students will interpret basic information and demonstrate their ability to determine relationships among facts, generalizations, definitions, and skills; Applying Concepts calls for the highest level of comprehension and inference; Writing Skills requires students to define or describe concepts in multiple sentence answers. Answers and objective correlations are provided in the *Teacher Guide and Answers* section.

Transparency Activities

Section Focus Transparencies: These transparencies are designed to generate interest and focus students' attention on the topics presented in the sections and/or to assess prior knowledge. There is a transparency for each section, or lesson, in the Student Edition. The reproducible student masters are located in the *Transparency Activities* section. The teacher material, located in the *Teacher Guide and Answers* section, includes Transparency Teaching Tips, a Content Background section, and Answers for each transparency.

Teaching Transparencies: These transparencies relate to major concepts that will benefit from an extra visual learning aid. Most of these transparencies contain diagrams/photos from the Student Edition. There is one *Teaching Transparency* for each chapter. The *Teaching Transparency Activity* includes a black-and-white reproducible master of the transparency accompanied by a student worksheet that reviews the concept shown in the transparency. These masters are found in the *Transparency Activities* section. The teacher material includes Transparency Teaching Tips, a Reteaching Suggestion, Extensions, and Answers to Student Worksheet. This teacher material is located in the *Teacher Guide and Answers* section.

Assessment Transparencies: An *Assessment Transparency* extends the chapter content and gives students the opportunity to practice interpreting and analyzing data presented in charts, graphs, and tables. Test-taking tips that help prepare students for success on standardized tests and answers to questions on the transparencies are provided in the *Teacher Guide and Answers* section.

Teacher Support and Planning

Content Outline for Teaching: These pages provide a synopsis of the chapter by section, including suggested discussion questions. Also included are the terms that fill in the blanks in the students' *Note-taking Worksheets*.

Spanish Resources: A Spanish version of the following chapter features are included in this section: objectives, vocabulary words and definitions, a chapter purpose, the chapter Activities, and content overviews for each section of the chapter.

Reproducible
Student Pages

Reproducible Student Pages

Hands-On
Activities

Modeling Earth's Farmland

Procedure

1. Cut an **apple** into four quarters and set aside three. One quarter of Earth's surface is land. The remaining 3/4 is covered with water.
2. Slice the remaining quarter into thirds.
3. Set aside two of the three pieces, because 2/3 of Earth's land is too hot, too cold, or too mountainous to farm or live on.
4. Carefully peel the remaining piece. This represents the usable land surface that must support the entire human population.

Analysis

What may happen if available farmland is converted to other uses?

_____

_____

_____

_____

Hands-On Activities

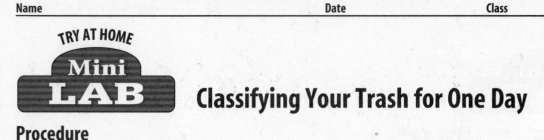

TRY AT HOME

Mini LAB

Classifying Your Trash for One Day

Procedure

1. Study the table below with the following columns; *Paper*, *Plastic*, *Glass*, *Metal*, and *Food Waste*.

2. Record items you throw out in one day. At the end of the day, count the number of trash items in each column.

3. Rank each column by number from the fewest trash items to the most trash items.

Data and Observations

	Paper	Plastic	Glass	Metal	Food Waste
Number of items					
Rank					

Analysis

1. Compare your rankings with those of others in your household.

_____

_____

_____

2. What activities can you change to decrease the amount of trash you produce?

_____

_____

_____

LAB What to wear?

Lab Preview

Directions: *Answer these questions before you begin the Lab.*

1. What is the intent of this lab?

   _____

2. What safety measures are specified?

   _____

What items in your house will end up in a landfill? You might think about milk jugs or food scraps. What about old clothing? In this lab, you'll observe what happens to different types of clothes that are buried in a landfill.

Real-World Question
Do materials decompose at the same rate?

Materials
identical baking trays (2)
garden soil
clothing made of natural fibers
   (linen, cotton, wool, silk)
clothing made of artificial materials
   (fleece, polyester, acrylic, rayon)
toothpicks
transparent tape
scissors
spray bottle filled with water

Goals
- **Compare** the decomposing rates of natural and artificial clothing materials.
- **Infer** the effect of these materials on landfills.

Safety Precautions

Procedure
1. Collect several articles of clothing and separate those made with natural fibers from those made from artificial materials.
2. Cut 3-cm squares of each type of clothing.
3. Cut 1-cm × 3-cm labels from a sheet of notebook paper, and write one label for each of your clothing squares. Tape each label to the tip of a toothpick.
4. Fill each tray halfway with garden soil. Lay your artificial cloth squares in one tray and your natural cloth squares in the other tray. Be certain the squares don't overlap. Thoroughly moisten all squares using the spray bottle.
5. Identify each clothing square by attaching a toothpick label.
6. Cover your squares with soil. Moisten the soil and place the trays in a dark place. Keep the soil moist for three weeks.
7. After three weeks, dig up your samples and observe each square. Record your observations in the table on the next page.

LAB (continued)

Data and Observations

Type of Fiber	Observations
Natural	
Artificial	

Conclude and Apply

1. **Compare** the amount of decomposition of the two types of materials.

_____

_____

_____

2. **Infer** the effects of clothing made with natural materials on landfills.

_____

_____

3. **Infer** the effects of clothing made with artificial materials on landfills.

_____

_____

4. **Research** materials used to manufacture clothing. Determine if the material is made from recycled products such as plastic bottles.

_____

_____

_____

Communicating Your Data

Compare the types of clothing worn by your classmates with the types you used in your experiment. Contrast the results of their experiments with your observations. **For more help, refer to the Science Skill Handbook.**

LAB A World Full of People

Lab Preview

Directions: *Answer these questions before you begin the Lab.*

1. What will you be showing in this lab?

_____

2. How many people does each object represent?

_____

Every second, five people are born on Earth and two or three people die. As a result, there is a net increase of two or three people in the world every second of every day. That amounts to about 81 million new people every year. This is nearly equal to the population of Central Africa. What effects will this rapid increase in human population have on Earth?

Real-World Question
How crowded will different regions of Earth become in the next ten years?

Materials
small objects such as popcorn kernels or dried
    beans (1,000)
large map of the world (the map must show
    the countries of the world)
clock or watch
calculator

Goals
- **Demonstrate** the world's human population increase in the next decade.
- **Predict** the world's population in 50 years.
- **Record, graph,** and **interpret** population data.

Safety Precautions 🥽 🧤
Never eat or taste anything in the lab, even if you are confident that you know what it is.

Procedure
1. Lay the map out on a table. The map represents Earth and the people already living here.
2. Each minute of time will represent one year. During your first minute, place 78 popcorn kernels on the continents of your map. Each kernel represents 1 million new people.
3. Place one kernel inside the borders of developed countries such as the United States, Canada, Japan, Australia, and countries in Europe. Place 77 kernels inside the borders of developing nations located in South America, Africa, and Asia.
4. Continue adding 78 kernels to your map in the same fashion each minute for 10 min. Record the total population increase for each year (each minute of the lab) in the data table in the Data and Observation section.

LAB (continued)

Data and Observations

Population Data	
Time (in years)	Total Population Increase

Analyze Your Data

1. **Draw and label** a graph of your data showing the time in years on the horizontal axis and the world population on the vertical axis.
2. **Calculate** the world's population in 50 years by using an average rate of 71 million people per year.
3. **Determine** world population in ten years if only 4.5 million people are added each year.

Conclude and Apply

1. **Infer** how many people will be added to Earth in the next ten years. Determine the world's

   population in ten years. _____

2. **Compare** the population growth in developed countries to the growth of developing countries.

   _____

3. **Discuss** ways the increase in the human population will affect Earth's resources in the future.

   _____

Communicating Your Data

Draw your graph on a computer and present your findings to the class. **For more help, refer to the Science Skill Handbook.**

Human Impact on the Environment

Human beings are changing the environment, and the rate at which they are changing it is increasing rapidly as the population increases. Only recently have people become aware of their impact on the atmosphere, water, and the crust of Earth.

Strategy

You will make a survey of your neighborhood or town to observe people's impact on the environment.

You will use the accompanying matrix to estimate the ways in which humans have affected your local environment.

You will suggest some ways people can change their impact on the environment.

Materials

clipboard
pencil

Procedure

1. Look over the check sheet on the next two pages. A, B, C, and D are general categories for the way people change the environment. Across the top are the various areas of the environment that may be affected by the processes and materials that people use.

2. Walk through your neighborhood (in the city, at least a 10-block square) taking the sheet with you.

3. Place a check after each type of environmental influence found in your neighborhood. For example, if new houses are being built, put a check after "houses," category A.

4. In the boxes to the right, put a diagonal slash under the area(s) affected by this influence. If the effect is good, put a plus in the lower right part of the box. If you think the effect is bad, place a minus in this position.

5. In the upper left of the box, place a number from 1 to 10 to indicate how much impact you think the change has had or will have. If you think the change is small, write in 1; if you think it is or will be very large, write in 10. Use your judgment and observations to assign numbers 2 through 9 on this impact scale.

6. Find your total for each influence and for each affected area. Record your totals in the chart.

7. Find the class total for each influence and for each affected area. Record those totals in the chart.

Laboratory Activity 1 (continued)

Data and Observations

Table 1

	Biological	Scenic	Recreation	Temperature	Air	Water	Eutrophi-cation	Other	Totals
A. Construction									
(Example)		2 / +				3 /	1 / -		2 / -
Houses									
Roads									
Transmission Lines									
Fences or other barriers									
Canals									
Dams									
Shore structures									
Cut and fill									
Tunnels									
Mines									
Industrial plants									
Landscaped lawns									
B. Traffic									
On roads									
Pipelines									
C. Chemicals									
Fertilization									
Weed and insect control									
Deicing highways									

Laboratory Activity 1 (continued)

Table 2

	Biological	Scenic	Recreation	Temperature	Air	Water	Eutrophi-cation	Other	Totals
D. Waste Disposal									
Litter and dumps									
Sewage									
Stack and exhaust emissions									
Cooling water discharge									
Used lubricant subhead									
Totals									
Class Totals									

Questions and Conclusions

1. List three ways in which the construction of concrete pavement (roads) changes the environment.

_____

_____

2. How does an automobile affect the atmosphere?

_____

3. What other methods of travel, other than automobile would have less adverse effects on the environment?

_____

_____

4. If there is smog in your local area, what is its source?

_____

5. What can be done to reduce or eliminate the smog?

_____

_____

6. What resources are being used in local construction?

_____

_____

Laboratory Activity 1 (continued)

7. What resources are lost to humans when cities move into the surrounding countryside?

_____

_____

8. Are there alternatives?

_____

_____

_____

_____

9. Discuss the drawbacks of the alternatives you have listed in the questions above.

_____

_____

_____

_____

_____

Strategy Check

_____ Can you recognize human influence on your local environment?

_____ Can you estimate the impact, good or bad, using the matrix?

_____ Can you suggest and evaluate alternatives?

LAB 2 Laboratory Activity

Reclamation of Mine Wastes

Mine wastes, which seem to be worthless, can be made profitable. For example, copper metal can be reclaimed from copper mine waste. When open pit copper is crushed and smelted, copper(II) sulfate is left in the waste rock. The copper(II) sulfate can be dissolved in water. Then more metallic copper can be removed by reacting the copper(II) sulfate with iron ores.

Strategy

You will investigate a process by which copper is reclaimed from open pit waste.
You will determine whether reclaiming copper is profitable.

Materials

copper(II) sulfate crystals, $CuSO_4$
balance
beaker (500-mL)
graduated cylinder (50-mL)
water
litmus paper (blue)
nails (iron scraps)

Procedure

1. Place 3 g of copper(II) sulfate in the beaker. **WARNING:** *Copper(II) sulfate is poisonous. Avoid contact with skin.*

2. Cover the copper(II) sulfate crystals with 50 mL of water. Record the color of the solution in Table 1. Test with litmus paper. Record your results in Table 1.

3. Place the iron scrap in the solution. Observe and record what happens in Table 1.

4. Test the solution with blue litmus paper and record your results in Table 1.

Data and Observations

Table 1

Solution	Color	Litmus	Other Observations
Copper(II) sulfate			
Copper(II) sulfate and iron			

Laboratory Activity 2 (continued)

Questions and Conclusions

1. Why did you add water to the copper(II) sulfate crystals?

_____

_____

2. What happens to the copper in the solution when iron is added?

_____

_____

3. Is this a chemical or physical method of reclaiming the copper?

_____

_____

4. What happened to the water in which the copper(II) sulfate is dissolved?

_____

_____

5. Does this method use up all the waste material?

_____

_____

6. What might happen to a stream if large amounts of the water used in this reclaiming process were flushed into it?

_____

_____

7. What might happen to an abandoned copper mine in a humid climate?

_____

_____

Strategy Check

_____ Can you recognize the copper deposit on the iron?

_____ Could copper be reclaimed from waste using this method?

_____ Would reclaiming the copper be profitable?

FOLDABLES
Reading & Study Skills

Our Impact on Land

Directions: *Use this page to label your Foldable at the beginning of the chapter.*

Know?

Like to know?

Learned?

Meeting Individual Needs

Directed Reading for Content Mastery

Overview
Our Impact on Land

Directions: *Complete the concept map using the terms in the list below.*

uses water	creates garbage	pollution from landfills
soil erosion	loss of forests	uses land	burns fossil fuels
cuts trees	air pollution	water pollution

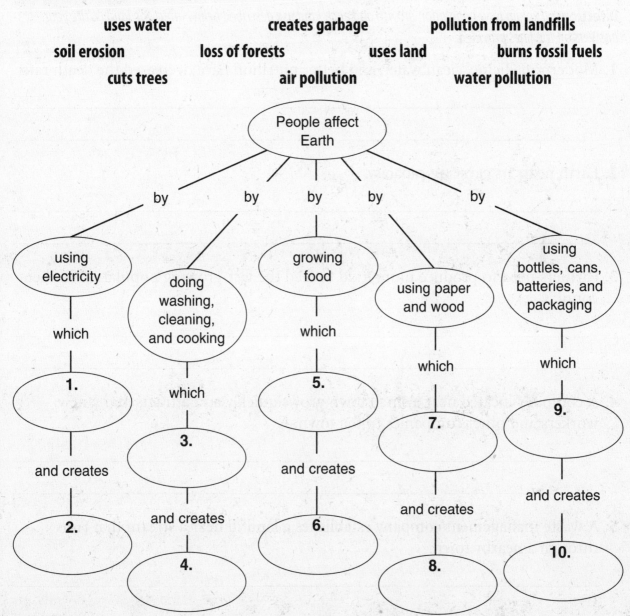

Directions: *Circle the term that correctly completes the sentences below.*

Earth is now experiencing a(n) **11.** (population/environment) explosion. Unless we use our resources wisely, Earth may reach its **12.** (outer limits/carrying capacity). All of us can work together to decrease the **13.** (fuels/pollutants) that are caused by our use of the land and its resources. We can conserve resources by reducing, reusing, and **14.** (revising/recycling).

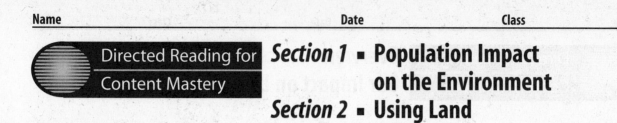

Directed Reading for
Content Mastery

Section 1 ▪ **Population Impact**
 on the Environment
Section 2 ▪ **Using Land**

Directions: *Explain how population growth and each land use described below affect the land. Write your answers on the lines provided.*

1. Modern medicine, clean water, and better nutrition have decreased the death rate.

_____

_____

2. Earth nears its carrying capacity.

_____

_____

3. Farmers need to produce more food to feed the fast-growing population in their country.

_____

_____

4. A company located near a small town grows quickly and attracts many new workers and other companies to the town.

_____

_____

5. A waste management company establishes a landfill near a stream that runs through a nearby town.

_____

_____

6. On a hot summer day, expressways around a large city are filled with cars and trucks.

_____

_____

Directed Reading for Content Mastery

Section 3 ▪ Conserving Resources

Directions: *Write the letter of the resource(s) that could be conserved by recycling each of the following.*

_____ 1. An aluminum beverage can

    a. energy   **b.** aluminum ore **c.** both

_____ 2. A stack of newspaper

    a. rocks   **b.** trees   **c.** plastic

_____ 3. A pile of food scraps

    a. nutrients   **b.** plastic   **c.** both

_____ 4. A plastic jug

    a. coal   **b.** oil   **c.** iron

Directions: *Answer the questions below on the lines provided.*

5. Why is the reuse of materials a way to conserve resources?

_____

6. How does reducing the use of packaging and other materials conserve resources?

_____

_____

7. How does walking rather than riding in a car save resources?

_____

8. What are the advantages of composting?

_____

_____

9. What are the disadvantages of recycling?

_____

_____

Meeting Individual Needs

Directed Reading for Content Mastery

Key Terms
Our Impact on Land

Directions: *Complete the following sentences using the terms listed below.*

stream discharge	composting	enzymes
conservation	sanitary landfills	population	hazardous wastes
pollutant	carrying capacity	recycling

1. We deposit much of our garbage in _____.

2. To reduce damage to the environment, people should practice

   _____ in using resources.

3. A _____ is the total number of individuals in

   an area.

4. Plants can help break down some organic pollutants, such as gasoline and oil,

   by releasing _____ into the soil.

5. Clogged sewer pipes and the runoff of rainwater from paved areas can increase

   _____ and cause floods.

6. _____ yard waste when you mow your lawn and

   rake leaves reduces the trash in landfills.

7. _____ means using materials again.

8. _____ are poisonous, cancer-causing, or

   flammable.

9. The largest number of individuals of a particular species that the environment

   will support is known as _____.

10. A _____ is a substance that contaminates the

    environment.

Lectura dirigida para el *Sinopsis*
Dominio del contenido **Nuestro impacto sobre el terreno**

Instrucciones: *Completa el mapa de conceptos usando los términos de la siguiente lista.*

usa agua   contaminación en vertederos controlados   crea basura

erosión del suelo   pérdida de bosques   usa terrenos   contaminación del aire

tala árboles   quema combustibles fósiles   contaminación del agua

Satisface las necesidades individuales

Instrucciones: *Haz un círculo alrededor del término que completa correctamente cada oración.*

La Tierra experimenta una explosión **11.** (demográfica/ambiental). A menos que usemos sabiamente nuestros recursos, la Tierra puede alcanzar su **12.** (límite exterior/capacidad de carga). Debemos cooperar para disminuir los **13.** (combustibles/contaminantes) que causa nuestro uso de la tierra y sus recursos. Al reducir, reutilizar y **14.** (revisar/reciclar) podemos conservar recursos.

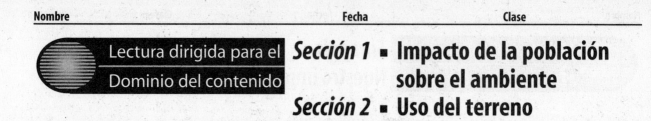

Lectura dirigida para el Dominio del contenido

Sección 1 ▪ Impacto de la población sobre el ambiente
Sección 2 ▪ Uso del terreno

Instrucciones: *Explica cómo el crecimiento demográfico y cada uno de los siguientes usos del terreno afectan el suelo. Escribe tus respuestas en las líneas dadas.*

1. La medicina moderna, el agua potable y una mejor nutrición han servido para disminuir la tasa de mortalidad.

_____

_____

2. La Tierra se aproxima a su capacidad de carga.

_____

_____

3. Los agricultores necesitan producir más alimentos para alimentar a una población nacional que crece rápidamente.

_____

_____

4. Una compañía localizada cerca de una pequeña ciudad crece rápidamente y atrae a muchos trabajadores nuevos y a otras compañías a la ciudad.

_____

_____

5. Una compañía de manejo de desechos establece un vertedero cerca de un arroyo que atraviesa un poblado cercano.

_____

_____

6. En un día caluroso de verano, las súper carreteras alrededor de una gran ciudad están llenas de autos y camiones.

_____

_____

Satisface las necesidades individuales

Lectura dirigida para el Dominio del contenido

Sección 3 ▪ Conserva los recursos

Instrucciones: *Escribe la letra correspondiente a los recursos que podrían conservarse si se reciclara cada uno de los siguientes.*

_____ 1. Una lata de gaseosa de aluminio

    a. energía   **b.** mena de aluminio   **c.** ambos

_____ 2. Pila de periódicos

    a. rocas   **b.** árboles   **c.** plástico

_____ 3. Pila de sobras de alimentos

    a. nutrientes   **b.** plástico   **c.** ambos

_____ 4. Jarra de plástico

    a. carbón   **b.** petróleo   **c.** hierro

Instrucciones: *Escribe tus respuestas en los espacios después de cada pregunta.*

5. ¿Por qué se conservan los recursos al reutilizar productos?

_____

6. ¿De qué forma ayuda la reducción de materiales de empaque y otros materiales a conservar recursos?

_____

_____

7. ¿De qué forma conserva recursos el caminar en lugar de usar el auto?

_____

8. ¿Cuáles son las ventajas de hacer abono orgánico?

_____

_____

9. ¿Cuáles son las desventajas de reciclar?

_____

_____

Satisface las necesidades individuales

Lectura dirigida para el Dominio del contenido *Términos claves* **Nuestro impacto sobre el terreno**

Instrucciones: *Completa las oraciones con los siguientes términos.*

cauce de corriente   hacer abono orgánico   enzimas
conservación   vertederos controlados   población   desechos peligrosos
contaminante   capacidad de carga   reciclaje

1. Depositamos gran parte de la basura en _____.

2. Para reducir los daños al ambiente, deberíamos practicar _____ en el uso de recursos.

3. Un(a) _____ es el número total de individuos en un área.

4. Las plantas pueden ayudar a desintegrar algunos contaminantes orgánicos, como la gasolina y el petróleo, al liberar _____ en el suelo.

5. Las cañerías de aguas negras atascadas y la escorrentía del agua de lluvia sobre las áreas pavimentadas pueden aumentar el(la) _____ y causar inundaciones.

6. Al _____ con los desechos de jardín después de cortar el césped y de recoger las hojas caídas de los árboles reduce la basura que se lleva a los vertederos.

7. El(La) _____ significa reutilizar los materiales.

8. Los(Las) _____ son venenosos, causan cáncer o son inflamables.

9. El mayor número de individuos de una especie que el ambiente puede sustentar se conoce como _____.

10. Un(a) _____ es una sustancia que contamina el ambiente.

SECTION 1 Reinforcement Population Impact on the Environment

Directions: *Answer the following questions on the lines provided.*

1. What did people long ago think about Earth's resources? Why is that earlier idea incorrect?

_____

_____

2. Define *population*.

_____

3. The term *population explosion* doesn't refer just to increased population, but to the rapid rate at which it is increasing. What does Figure 2 in your textbook show about the speed at which our world's population has increased?

_____

4. How has our improved understanding of nutrition contributed to overpopulation?

_____

5. What problems could people on Earth face if the population explosion continues?

_____

Directions: *Complete the following chart using the words listed below.*

electricity use   water use   farming

packaging products   making products

Effects on the environment	Caused by
6. Generated by burning fuels, which pollute the atmosphere	
7. Pollutes the water; cleaning the water adds substances such as chlorine to the environment	
8. Erodes topsoil	
9. Uses gasoline to transport resources; processes used to make products add pollutants	
10. Using plastic involves refining oil, which produces many pollutants; using paper involves cutting down trees and producing pollutants to transform trees into paper	

SECTION 2 Reinforcement Using Land

Directions: *Decide which of the following effects on the environment are due to natural causes and which are due to the actions of people. Write* **natural** *if the cause is natural. Write* **people** *if the cause is people.*

_____ 1. Fires are set by lightning in a national forest.

_____ 2. Groundwater near a sanitary landfill that is close to a school is found to be radioactive.

_____ 3. An earthquake causes damage in some homes.

_____ 4. Increasing amounts of herbicides and pesticides are found in rivers and groundwater.

_____ 5. A woodland area in Pennsylvania is torn up for coal mining.

_____ 6. Topsoil becomes dust and is blown from farms in a midwestern state.

_____ 7. A beach is eroded by high waves.

_____ 8. The landfills in a large city are overflowing, and the city wants to ship its garbage to a landfill on an island south of the United States.

_____ 9. A small country can no longer feed its growing population.

_____ 10. Some suburbs cannot find landfill room for the grass clippings and leaves collected.

Directions: *Answer the following questions on the lines provided.*

11. Write the number of the first item above that you decided was due to people. What would you want to be sure of first if you were called in to solve the problem?

_____

_____

12. Write the number of the last item above that you decided was due to people. What would you recommend to the people in that area?

_____

_____

_____

13. Which effects might be due to farming methods?

_____

14. Which effects could be lessened if most people practiced conservation by reusing and recycling materials? Explain your answers.

_____

_____

_____

Meeting Individual Needs

SECTION 3 Reinforcement Conserving Resources

Directions: *Answer the following questions on the lines provided.*

1. What is a recyclable object?

_____

2. Give three reasons why paper should be recycled.

_____

_____

_____

3. Why should aluminum be recycled?

_____

4. How do container laws encourage recycling?

_____

_____

5. How much does recycling reduce the amount of trash a person generates in a lifetime?

_____

6. List two ways governments encourage recycling.

_____

_____

7. List three ways you can reduce your consumption of materials at school and at home.

_____

_____

_____

_____

8. Do you think governments should require recycling? Why or why not?

_____

_____

_____

_____

Enrichment   Predicting Population Growth

In this chapter, you read about population growth. Here are some new facts along with some facts from the chapter:

- The United Nations keeps track of population statistics for the world.
- World population grows each year because the number of the births per year is greater than the number of deaths per year.
- In 2000, the world population was 6.05 billion people.
- The population of the world is increasing by about 93 million people per year.

1. What was the population in the year 2000? _____

2. Suppose the world population increases by one percent per year. Do you think, without figuring it out, that a one percent increase would result in a big increase in the number of people? Now figure out how many people a one percent increase of the 2000 population represents.

   _____

3. Suppose the world population increases by two percent per year. How many people does a two percent increase of the 2000 population represent?

   _____

4. How does the predicted increase of 93 million people per year compare with the percentage increases you just calculated?

   _____

5. Some people hope the world will reach a zero population growth. What do you think this means in relation to the number of births and deaths per year?

   _____

   _____

6. If zero population growth had been achieved by the year 2000 and continued, what would be the population in 2020? Explain.

   _____

   _____

   _____

7. Why do you think the United Nations keeps information on world population growth?

   _____

   _____

   _____

SECTION 2 Enrichment — A return to the old days?

Andes Mountains

La Paz

Lake Titicaca 3812 m

Sucre

Altiplano 3600–3800 m

PERU

Pacific Ocean

BOLIVIA

CHILE

Meeting Individual Needs

Some farmers near Lake Titicaca in Bolivia are trying to feed their own people by using a very old technology that had been forgotten for centuries. About A.D. 500, the Tiahuanaco civilization dominated the highland plateau of Bolivia (called the Altiplano). The civilization disappeared about A.D. 1200 for unknown reasons. Its successful system of farming was never used again. About 750 years later, archaeologists uncovered the remains of the system and determined how it worked. In the middle 1980s, scientists from Bolivia and the United States began to work with Aymara farmers to rebuild part of the system.

Ancient Raised Gardens

The system is called raised-bed agriculture. Growing platforms 1.5 meters deep and about 15 wide by 180 meters long are constructed with thick rock bases. The rock is covered with a layer of clay and a layer of fine gravel or sand to provide drainage. Fertile topsoil is added.

A carefully planned system of canals carries water to the crops. In times of heavy rain, the canals divert the rain from the beds.

Solar Energy and Conservation

The canal water is heated by the sun during the day and radiates enough warmth at night to protect the crops from frost. Decaying plants are scooped out of the canals and used for fertilizer. Topsoil for the raised beds is dug from the canals. No chemicals are used.

An Old System Works Again

Using only seeds and basic farming equipment, today's Aymaras have increased their potato crop yield seven times. By developing the system more widely, these farmers may be able to solve Bolivia's food shortage, which is a chief cause of poverty in the nation. Other farmers are eager to be part of the program. They are pleased to be using ideas developed by their ancient ancestors.

1. Why do you think the farmers needed to protect their crops against frost at night? (Look at the map for a clue.)

_____

2. Review the main topics in the lesson on land usage in your text. Write a one- or two-paragraph paper telling how an experiment like the one in Bolivia can help the world.

SECTION 3   Enrichment   Moving Day

Meeting Individual Needs

Imagine that your family is moving. You and your sister and brother are responsible for everything in your rooms except the furniture. You are to pack what you want to take, dispose of what you don't want, and leave nothing in the house.

The evening you are to pack, you're the last one to arrive home and find your brother and sister have been very efficient. They tell you they've finished their sorting. The hallway is filled with large plastic bags. Each bag is numbered and labeled. You examine them carefully. The labels read as follows:

- old toys—trash
- summer clothes—move
- old records—trash
- old clothes—trash
- old makeup and medicine—trash

- Books—move
- tapes and CD's—move
- school papers—trash
- science experiments from school—trash
- dead plants—trash

Of course you realize your brother and sister need to have conservation explained to them. Suggest they change their containers and explain why.

Directions: *To help them re-sort their belongings, fill in the chart below showing how to organize the things they want to get rid of. Suggest which items may be separated for reuse and recycling. Show them safe ways to dispose of other trash.*

Category	Trash items
1. Kind of packing containers to use	
2. Reusable items	
3. Recyclable items	
4. Hazardous items	
5. Compost	

Note-taking Worksheet   Our Impact on Land

Section 1   Population Impact on the Environment

A. _____—all of the individuals of one species living in the same area at the

same time

   1. Population explosion—Earth's population is _____ rapidly.

      a. Medicine, clean water, and _____ have lowered the death rate.

      b. Number of _____ has increased because more people live to child-bearing age.

   2. By 2050, Earth's population is predicted to reach _____ billion.

B. Earth has a _____—the largest number of individuals of a particular species

the environment will support.

C. People affect the environment by:

   1. Using _____, which is sometimes produced by burning _____.

      a. The environment changes when fossil fuels are _____.

      b. The environment changes again when fossil fuels are _____.

   2. Eating food

      a. It takes _____ to grow food.

      b. Farmers use _____ to grow food, which can get into water supplies

and threaten other species.

   3. Using _____

      a. Made from _____

      b. Refining oil produces _____—substances that contaminate the environment.

   4. Using _____

      a. _____ are cut down.

      b. Water and _____ are given off in the papermaking process.

   5. Producing _____, which must be disposed of somewhere

Meeting Individual Needs

Note-taking Worksheet (continued)

Section 2   Using Land

A. Farming—To feed people, farmers try to grow more and better crops.

   1. Some farming practices _____ the amount of food grown on parcels of land.

      a. _____ fertilizers

      b. _____ and pesticides

   2. Other practices can reduce environmental damage, such as _____.

      a. _____ farming—natural fertilizers, crop rotation, biological pest controls

      b. _____—planting seeds between previous year's stubble to save topsoil

      c. _____—Rows are tilled across hills and valleys to capture water and soil,
      reducing erosion.

B. Growing food for _____

   1. Animals eat _____ and are then used as food for _____.

   2. Land is used for _____ and to grow _____ for cattle.

C. Forest Resources—Deforestation occurs for _____, _____, _____, or
_____.

   1. _____ become extinct each year due to the loss of forests, especially _____.
   forests.

   2. Deforestation has an impact on _____ and _____.

   3. Local regions may receive less _____.

D. Development—building highways, office buildings, stores, and parking lots

   1. Paving prevents _____ from soaking easily into the soil.

   2. Instead, it runs off into streams and _____.

      a. Stream discharge—the _____ of water flowing past a point per unit of time

      b. In _____ areas, heavy rainwater can lead to increased stream discharge, causing
      flooding.

   3. Paving prevents rainwater from refilling underground _____.

Meeting Individual Needs

Note-taking Worksheet (continued)

E. **Sanitary landfills**—areas where daily _____ is deposited and covered with soil

  1. Lined with _____ to prevent pollutants from leaking into soil or groundwater

  2. Many materials do no not _____ in landfills.

  3. As landfills fill up, new ones must be built.

F. **Hazardous wastes**—wastes that are _____, that cause cancer, or that can catch fire

  1. In many states, they cannot be deposited in _____.

  2. Some can be _____.

  3. Phytoremediation—using _____ to clean up the soil by removing metals from it

  4. _____ from plant roots increase the rate that organic pollutants break down and become harmless.

G. _____—land that is set aside to protect it from environmental problems caused by people

Section 3   Conserving Resources

A. **Conservation**—the careful use of _____ to reduce damage to the environment

B. Ways to conserve resources

  1. _____—using less materials

  2. _____—finding another use for an item rather than throwing it away

    a. _____—piling yard wastes where they can decompose gradually

    b. If everyone in the country used composting, _____ percent less trash would be put in landfills each year.

  3. _____—using materials again by converting used materials into new and useful products

  4. These processes can save _____, reduce _____, and minimize the need to _____.

Assessment

Chapter Review

Our Impact on Land

Part A. Vocabulary Review

Directions: *Use the following words and phrases to fill in the blanks below.*

composting	carrying capacity	pollutant	stream discharge
population	hazardous waste	recycling	conservation
enzymes	sanitary landfill	carbon dioxide	radioactive

1. The total number of individuals of a particular species in an area is called

   _____.

2. An area where waste is deposited is properly called a _____.

3. The maximum number of individuals of a particular type that the planet will support is

   Earth's _____.

4. Piling grass and leaves where they can gradually decompose

   is called _____.

5. Processing an object to be used again is _____.

6. A waste material that is dangerous to organisms is

   called _____.

7. The careful use of resources that reduces damage to the environment

   is _____.

8. _____ speed up chemical reactions.

9. A substance that contaminates the environment is called

   a _____.

10. _____ is the volume of water flowing past a point per

    unit of time.

11. More _____ may be trapped in the atmosphere when forests
    are cut down because there are fewer plants to photosynthesize.

12. _____ waste produced by nuclear power plants, hospitals,
    and other sources may be around for thousands of years.

Assessment

Chapter Review (continued)

Part B. Concept Review

Directions: *Answer the following questions on the lines provided.*

1. What effect has modern medicine had on the world's population?

2. List two other factors that have affected population and resulted in a larger population.

3. In what ways does the use of plastic change the environment?

4. How does the energy used by an average person living in the United States compare with the energy used by the average person living elsewhere in the world?

5. Does farming adversely affect the environment? Explain.

6. Which will feed more people, a square kilometer of vegetable crops or a square kilometer used to raise livestock?

7. In what ways does cutting the rain forest affect the environment?

8. How can paving over the land affect the environment?

9. What does recycling do for the environment?

⬤ **Chapter Test** **Our Impact on Land**

I. Testing Concepts

Directions: *Identify each statement as* **true** *or* **false**. *Rewrite false statements to make them correct.*

_____ 1. Each day about 500,000 people are added to Earth's population.

_____

_____ 2. Paving over land causes little damage to the environment.

_____

_____ 3. Recycling saves natural resources and reduces damage to the environment.

_____

_____ 4. Sanitary landfills are lined to help lessen groundwater pollution.

_____

_____ 5. When forests disappear, animal species may also disappear.

_____

_____ 6. A container law requires a refundable deposit on all trash.

_____

_____ 7. Because sanitary landfills are lined, hazardous substances cannot leak into the soil.

_____

_____

_____ 8. The average person in the United States uses several times the energy used by the average person elsewhere in the world.

_____

_____

_____ 9. Developed countries use more resources than developing countries.

_____

_____

_____ 10. The term *composting* means piling up grass and leaves so they can be collected.

_____

Chapter Test (continued)

Directions: *For each of the following, write the letter of the term or phrase that best completes the sentence.*

_____ 11. Population explosion refers to the _____.
a. estimated world population in 2025
b. number of people who live in poverty
c. world population in 1810
d. increased rate at which the population is growing

_____ 12. One example of a program that encourages recycling is _____.
a. the development of paper products made of recycled material
b. a five-cent refundable deposit is made on beverage containers
c. people pay higher trash collection fees if they recycle
d. new jobs are created in "reuse" industries

_____ 13. One disadvantage to recycling is _____.
a. more trucks and people needed to haul materials
b. a five-cent refundable deposit on beverage cans
c. a growing population
d. a lower trash collection fee

_____ 14. One cause of the population explosion is _____.
a. air pollution   b. poor nutrition   c. better nutrition   d. water pollution

_____ 15. Reduced vegetation on Earth may result in _____.
a. a localized decrease in rainfall
b. increased habitats
c. less room for humans
d. more oxygen in the atmosphere

_____ 16. The ways each person in a developed country affects the environment include _____.
a. generating waste   c. treating water to clean it
b. using fossil fuels for energy   d. all of the above

_____ 17. A land use that **DOES NOT** change the environment _____.
a. grazing livestock   c. setting aside natural preserves
b. using herbicides   d. cutting trees

_____ 18. Recycling materials helps save _____.
a. energy   b. landfill space   c. both a and b   d. neither a nor b

_____ 19. A growing population puts demands on the land for _____.
a. food   b. living space   c. landfills for trash   d. all of these

_____ 20. A person in a developed country can help protect the environment by _____.
a. using more energy   c. cutting down trees
b. using less energy   d. creating trash for landfills

Chapter Test (continued)

II. Understanding Concepts

Skill: Making an Outline

Directions: *Insert the number of the correct phrase below to complete the outline at the right.*

How People Affect Earth

I. Farming the land

   A. _____

   B. _____

II. Paving over the land

   A. _____

   B. _____

III. Cutting trees

   A. _____

   B. _____

1. Erosion from tilling the soil

2. Habitat destruction

3. Species extinction

4. Pollution from herbicides

5. Reduction of water in underground supplies

6. Increased risk of flooding

Skill: Using Graphs

Directions: *Use the graph below, which shows the population growth of modern humans, to answer the questions.*

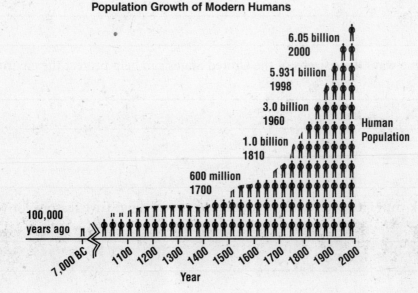

Population Growth of Modern Humans

7. What was the population in 1960? _____

8. How many years did it take for the population to grow from 1 billion to 3 billion? _____

9. By how many more people did the population increase between 1700 and 1810? _____

10. About when did the human species first appear? _____

Chapter Test (continued)

III. Applying Concepts

Writing Skills

Directions: *Answer the following questions using complete sentences.*

1. People who live in the United States use several times as much energy as an average person elsewhere in the world. Explain some ways the activities of a person in the United States may affect the environment.

_____

_____

_____

2. If a law required all newspapers in the nation to use recycled paper for Sunday issues, and it takes 500,000 trees for one Sunday's issues nationwide, how many trees would be saved in one year? How would this affect the environment?

_____

_____

_____

3. How can the design of a sanitary landfill reduce air, soil, and water pollution?

_____

_____

4. What are some ways the citizens of the United States can help protect the environment?

_____

_____

_____

5. Do you think your city government should require recycling? Give reasons for your answer.

_____

_____

_____

_____

Assessment

Transparency
Activities

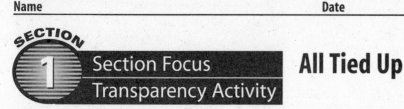

SECTION
1 Section Focus
Transparency Activity

All Tied Up

More and more we are seeing traffic situations like this one all across the country. Our ever increasing population means even more drivers—and vehicles—on the roads.

1. Do you think this road has reached its limit to carry traffic? Explain.

2. Is building bigger roads a good solution to this problem? Why or why not?

3. How might it be possible to have more people, but less traffic?

Transparency Activities

Land and Water

Wetlands are places like bogs, swamps, and marshes. Wetlands have the capacity to absorb a great deal of water, and, in doing so, they protect other areas from floods.

1. How can a wetland protect another area from floods?

2. How might this flood be avoided?

Transparency Activities

Relaxin' on the Refuse

Plastic refuse usually doesn't make an attractive seat. However with a little effort, it can be reused in a variety of very useful ways. The bench and paving stones you see here are made of reused plastic, so pull up a seat!

1. How might reusing material help preserve the environment?

2. What kinds of things might be reused?

Transparency Activities

Teaching Transparency
Activity

Destruction of the Rain Forest

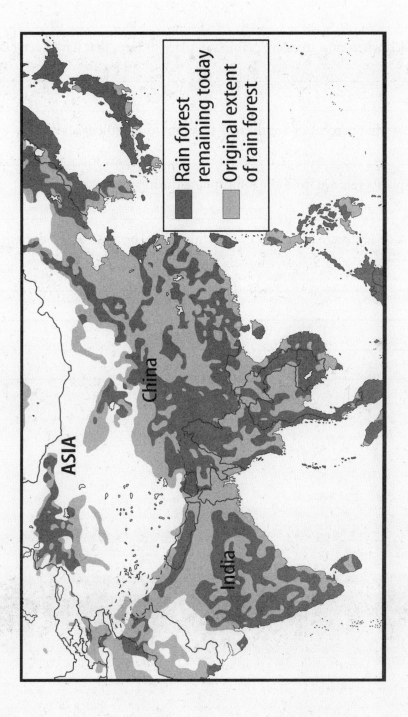

Rain forest remaining today

Original extent of rain forest

China

ASIA

India

Transparency Activities

Teaching Transparency Activity (continued)

1. What might result from the destruction of rain forests?

   _____

   _____

   _____

   _____

2. What is it called when new trees are planted in place of trees that have been cut down?

   _____

   _____

3. Approximately what percent of Southeast Asia's rain forest still exists?

   _____

4. What gas do plants remove from the atmosphere during photosynthesis?

   _____

5. If carbon dioxide levels are increased in the atmosphere because of the decreasing rain forest, what could result?

   _____

   _____

   _____

   _____

Assessment Transparency Activity

Our Impact on Land

Directions: Carefully review the table and answer the following questions.

Average Water Usage for Household Activities			
Activity	Water used per activity (L)	Times done per day	Water used per day (L)
Washing a load of clothes	227.1	1	227.1
Washing a load of dishes	94.6	1	94.6
Taking a shower	94.6	3	283.8
Flushing the toilet	26.5	18	477.0

1. According to the table, we can conclude that it takes ____.
   A the same amount of water to flush the toilet as it does to take a shower
   B the same amount of water to wash one load of dishes as it does to wash a load of clothes
   C more water to wash clothes than to wash a load of dishes
   D more water to flush the toilet than it does to wash a load of dishes

2. More water is commonly spent flushing the toilet than washing clothes each day because ____.
   F washing a load of clothes uses very little water
   G toilets are flushed several times in a single day
   H water used by washing machines is recycled
   J clothes are washed several times a day

Transparency Activities

Teacher Support and Planning

Teacher Support and Planning

Content Outline for Teaching: Our Impact on Land

Section 1   Population Impact on the Environment

> Underlined words and phrases are to be filled in by students on their version of the outline.

A. <u>**Population**</u>—all of the individuals of one species living in the same area at the same time

   1. Population explosion—Earth's population is <u>increasing</u> rapidly.

     a. Medicine, clean water, and <u>better nutrition</u> have lowered the death rate.

     b. Number of <u>births</u> has increased because more people live to child-bearing age.

   2. By 2050, Earth's population is predicted to reach <u>9</u> billion.

B. Earth has a <u>**carrying capacity**</u>—the largest number of individuals of a particular species the environment will support.

C. People affect the environment by:

   1. Using <u>electricity</u>, which is sometimes produced by burning <u>fossil fuels</u>

     a. The environment changes when fossil fuels are <u>mined</u>.

     b. The environment changes again when fossil fuels are <u>burned</u>.

   2. Eating food

     a. It takes <u>land</u> to grow food.

     b. Farmers use <u>chemical substances</u> to grow food, which can get into water supplies and threaten other species.

   3. Using <u>plastics</u>

     a. Made from <u>oil</u>

     b. Refining oil produces <u>**pollutants**</u>—substances that contaminate the environment.

   4. Using <u>paper</u>

     a. <u>Trees</u> are cut down.

     b. Water and <u>air pollutants</u> are given off in the papermaking process.

   5. Producing <u>waste</u>, which must be disposed of somewhere

DISCUSSION QUESTION:

What are the impacts on the environment when you use your car to go get food at a fast food restaurant? *The car burns fossil fuels, which releases pollutants into the air. The fast food restaurant uses paper to package the food, so trees were cut down and air pollutants were given off when the paper was made. The restaurant also uses plastic to package the food, which released pollutants and used up oil. It took land and possibly chemical substances to grow the food, and those chemical substances could get into the water supply or threaten other species. Finally, the packaging created garbage.*

Content Outline for Teaching (continued)

Section 2   Using Land

A. Farming—To feed people, farmers try to grow more and better crops.

1. Some farming practices <u>increase</u> the amount of food grown on parcels of land.

   a. <u>Chemical</u> fertilizers

   b. <u>Herbicides</u> and pesticides

2. Other practices can reduce environmental damage such as <u>soil erosion</u>.

   a. <u>Organic</u> farming—natural fertilizers, crop rotation, biological pest controls

   b. <u>No-till farming</u>—planting seeds between previous year's stubble to save topsoil

   c. <u>Contour plowing</u>—Rows are tilled across hills and valleys to capture water and soil.

B. Growing food for <u>livestock</u>

1. Animals eat <u>vegetation</u> and are then used as food for <u>humans</u>.

2. Land is used for <u>pasture</u> and to grow <u>crops</u> for cattle.

C. Forest Resources—Deforestation occurs for <u>agriculture</u>, <u>grazing</u>, <u>development</u>, or <u>logging</u>.

1. <u>Species</u> become extinct each year due to the loss of forests, especially <u>rain</u> forests.

2. Deforestation has an impact on <u>plants</u> and <u>animals</u>.

3. Local regions may receive less <u>rainfall</u>.

D. Development—building, highways, office buildings, stores, and parking lots

1. Paving prevents <u>water</u> from soaking easily into the soil.

2. Instead, it runs off into streams and <u>sewers</u>.

   a. **Stream discharge**—the <u>volume</u> of water flowing past a point per unit of time

   b. In <u>paved</u> areas, heavy rainwater can lead to increased stream discharge, causing flooding.

3. Paving prevents rainwater from refilling underground <u>water supplies</u>

E. **Sanitary landfills**—areas where daily <u>garbage</u> is deposited and covered with soil

1. Lined with <u>plastic, concrete, or clay-rich soil</u> to prevent pollutants from leaking into soil or groundwater

2. Many materials do no not <u>decompose</u> in landfills.

3. As landfills fill up, new ones must be built.

Content Outline for Teaching (continued)

F. **Hazardous wastes**—wastes that are <u>poisonous</u>, that cause cancer, or that can catch fire

   1. In many states, they cannot be deposited in <u>sanitary landfills</u>

   2. Some can be <u>recycled.</u>

   3. Phytoremediation—using <u>plants</u> to clean up the soil by removing metals from it

   4. <u>Enzymes</u> from plant roots increase the rate that organic pollutants break down.

G. <u>Natural preserves</u>—land that is set aside to protect it from environmental problems caused by people

DISCUSSION QUESTION:

What may happen if our rain forests continue to disappear? *Many species that live in the rain forests will become extinct. We may experience more carbon dioxide in the atmosphere, because fewer plants will be absorbing it. The surrounding regions may receive less rainfall, because there will be less water from tree leaves to evaporate into the air.*

Section 3 Conserving Resources

A. **Conservation**—the careful use of <u>resources</u> to reduce damage to the environment

B. Ways to conserve resources

   1. <u>Reducing</u>—Using less materials

   2. <u>Reusing</u>—finding another use for an item rather than throwing it away

     a. **Composting**—piling yard wastes where they can decompose gradually

     b. If everyone in the country used composting, <u>20</u> percent less trash would be put in landfills each year.

   3. <u>Recycling</u>—using materials again by converting used materials into new and useful products

   4. These processes can save <u>landfill space</u>, reduce <u>energy use</u>, and minimize the need to <u>extract raw materials from Earth</u>.

DISCUSSION QUESTION:

What can you do to conserve resources? *I can recycle my pop cans. I can bring my lunch in a reusable container rather than throwing away paper or plastic bags every day. I can recycle the paper I do my homework on.*

Nuestro impacto sobre el terreno

SECCIÓN 1 Impacto de la población sobre el ambiente

Lo que aprenderás

- A describir la velocidad de crecimiento de la población humana.
- A identificar razones del rápido crecimiento de la población humana de la Tierra.
- A enumerar maneras en las que las personas pueden afectar el ambiente.

Por qué es importante

Al crecer la población humana, los recursos se agotan y se producen más desechos.

Vocabulario

population / población: número total de individuos de una misma especie que ocupa la misma área.

carrying capacity / capacidad de carga: número máximo de individuos de una especie dada que el ambiente puede mantener.

pollutant / contaminante: cualquier sustancia que contamina el ambiente.

SECCIÓN 2 Uso del terreno

Lo que aprenderás

- A identificar las formas en que se usa la tierra.
- A explicar cómo el uso de la tierra crea problemas ambientales.
- A identificar lo que puedes hacer para proteger el ambiente.

Por qué es importante

El uso responsable de la tierra ayudará a conservar este recurso natural.

Vocabulario

stream discharge / descarga de corriente: volumen de agua que fluye por un punto específico por unidad de tiempo.

sanitary landfill / vertedero controlado: área en donde la basura es depositada y cubierta con tierra; está diseñado para prevenir la contaminación del terreno y del agua.

hazardous waste / desechos peligrosos: desechos venenosos, inflamables o carcinógenos.

enzyme / enzima: proteína que acelera las reacciones químicas en los organismos.

LABORATORIO ¿Qué te pondrás?

¿Qué artículos de tu casa terminarán en un vertedero? Puedes pensar en los envases para la leche o restos de alimentos. ¿Pero qué de la ropa vieja? En este laboratorio observarás lo que le sucede a los diferentes tipos de artículos de vestir que se entierran en un vertedero.

Preguntas del mundo real

¿Se descomponen todos los materiales a la misma velocidad?

Metas

- **Comparar** las tasas de descomposición de los materiales para ropa naturales y artificiales.
- **Inferir** el efecto de estos materiales en los vertederos.

Materiales

bandejas de hornear idénticas (2)
suelo para jardín
ropa hecha de fibras naturales (lino, algodón, lana, seda)
ropa hecha de fibras artificiales (lanilla, poliéster, acrílico, rayón, nilón)
palillos de dientes
cinta adhesiva transparente
tijeras
botella rociadora con agua

Procedimiento

1. Recoge varios artículos de ropa y sepáralos como hechos de fibras naturales o de materiales artificiales.
2. Corta cuadrados de 3 cm de lado de cada tipo de material.
3. Corta etiquetas de 1 cm por 3 cm de una hoja de papel y escribe una etiqueta para cada tipo de material. Adhiere cada etiqueta a la punta de un palillo de dientes.
4. Llena las bandejas hasta la mitad con suelo de jardín. Pon los cuadrados de tela artificial en una bandeja y los de tela natural en la otra. Asegúrate de que los cuadrados no se sobrepongan. Moja completamente cada cuadrado con la botella rociadora.
5. Identifica cada tipo de material insertando la etiqueta con el palillo.
6. Cubre los cuadrados con suelo. Humedece el suelo y coloca las dos bandejas en un sitio oscuro. Mantén el suelo húmedo durante tres semanas.
7. Después de tres semanas, saca tus muestras y observa cada cuadrado. Anota tus observaciones en el Diario de ciencias.

Concluye y aplica

1. **Compara** la cantidad de descomposición entre los dos tipos de materiales.
2. **Infiere** los efectos de la ropa hecha de telas naturales sobre los vertederos.
3. **Infiere** los efectos de la ropa hecha de telas artificiales sobre los vertederos.
4. **Investiga** los materiales que se usan para hacer ropa. Determina si las telas se hacen de productos reciclados como botellas plásticas.

Comunica tus datos

Compara los tipos de ropa que usaron tus compañeros con los que usaste tú en tu laboratorio. **Para más ayuda, consulta el Science Skill Handbook.**

3 Conserva los recursos

Lo que aprenderás

- A identificar tres formas de conservación de recursos.
- A explicar las ventajas del reciclaje.

Por qué es importante

La conservación de recursos ayuda a reducir los desechos sólidos.

Vocabulario

conservation / conservación: uso cuidadoso de los recursos para disminuir el daño al ambiente a través de métodos como el abono orgánico y el reciclaje de los materiales.

composting / abono orgánico: método de conservación en que los desperdicios del jardín, como el pasto, la maleza y las hojas rastrilladas, se amontonan y se dejan descomponer gradualmente.

recycling / reciclaje: método de conservación en que los materiales se utilizan nuevamente.

LABORATORIO Un mundo lleno de gente

Cada segundo nacen cinco personas en la Tierra y dos o tres personas mueren. Como resultado, hay un aumento neto de dos o tres personas en el mundo cada segundo de cada día. Esto llega a ser cerca de 78 millones de personas nuevas al año. Esto es casi igual a la población de África central. ¿Qué efectos tendrá este rápido crecimiento de la población humana sobre la Tierra?

Preguntas del mundo real

¿Cuántos habitantes habrá en diferentes regiones del mundo en los próximos diez años?

Metas
- **Demostrar** el aumento en la población humana mundial en la próxima década.
- **Predecir** la población mundial en 50 años.
- **Anotar, graficar** e **interpretar** datos sobre poblaciones.

Materiales
objetos pequeños como granos de maíz o chícharos secos (1,000)
mapa del mundo grande (el mapa debe mostrar los países del mundo)
reloj
calculadora

Medidas de seguridad 🥽 🧤
Nunca comas ni bebas nada del laboratorio, aún si crees saber lo que es.

Procedimiento
1. Copia la tabla de datos en tu Diario de ciencias.
2. Pon el mapa sobre una mesa. El mapa representa la Tierra y las personas que la habitan.
3. Cada minuto representará un año. Durante tu primer minuto coloca 95 granos de maíz sobre los continentes de tu mapa. Cada grano representa 1 millón de personas más.
4. Coloca un grano dentro de los límites de los países desarrollados como Estados Unidos, Canadá, Japón, Australia y los países de Europa. Coloca 77 granos dentro de los límites de los países en desarrollo localizados en Sur América, África y Asia.
5. Continúa añadiendo 78 granos a tu mapa de la misma manera durante 10 minutos. Anota el aumento total de la población cada año (cada minuto de la tabla) en tu tabla de datos.

Analiza tus datos
1. **Dibuja y rotula** un gráfico con tus datos que muestre el tiempo en años en el eje horizontal y la población mundial en el eje vertical.
2. **Calcula** la población mundial en 50 años usando una tasa promedio de 71 millones de personas por año.

3. **Determina** la población del mundo en 10 años si sólo se agregaran 4.5 millones de personas por año.

Datos sobre población	
Tiempo (años)	Aumento total de la población
1	95 millones
2	190 millones
3	285 millones
4	380 millones
5	425 millones
6	570 millones
7	665 millones
8	760 millones
9	855 millones
10	950 millones

Concluye y aplica
1. **Infiere** cuántas personas nuevas nacerán en la Tierra en los próximos 10 años. Determina la población mundial en 10 años.
2. **Compara** el crecimiento demográfico en los países desarrollados con el crecimiento en los países en desarrollo.
3. **Habla** sobre maneras en que el aumento en la población humana afectará los recursos de la Tierra en el futuro.

Comunica tus datos
Dibuja tu gráfico en una computadora y presenta tus descubrimiento a la clase. **Para más ayuda, consulta el Science Skill Handbook.**

Guía de estudio

Repasa las ideas principales

Sección 1 Impacto de la población sobre el ambiente

1. La medicina moderna, el agua limpia y la mejor nutrición han contribuido a la explosión en el crecimiento de la población humana de la Tierra.
2. Los recursos de la Tierra son limitados.
3. Nuestras actividades diarias usan recursos y producen desechos. *¿Qué recursos se consumieron para producir los artículos que se muestran aquí?*

Sección 2 Uso del terreno

1. La tierra se usa para la agricultura, la ganadería, para obtener madera, para la urbanización y para deshacerse de los desechos.
2. La agricultura y la urbanización son formas de uso de la tierra que tienen impacto sobre el ambiente. En la agricultura se usan sustancias químicas. *¿Cuáles son algunos de los efectos del suelo pavimentado?*

3. El uso de los recursos forestales tiene impacto sobre los organismos y el clima de la Tierra.
4. A veces se usan plantas para desintegrar y absorber contaminantes de áreas contaminadas.
5. Las nuevas tecnologías han reducido en gran medida la necesidad de deshacerse de los desechos peligrosos.
6. Una manera de preservar nuestra Tierra es proteger áreas naturales.

Sección 3 Conserva los recursos

1. Reciclar, reducir y reutilizar materiales son maneras importantes de conservar los recursos naturales. *¿Cómo puedes reciclar los desechos de jardín, tal como este pasto cortado?*
2. El reducir, reutilizar y reciclar los artículos de consumo ha hecho disminuir los depósitos anuales de basura en los vertederos desde 1980.
3. Se pueden usar diferentes métodos para estimular el reciclaje.

Hands-On Activities

MiniLAB (page 3)
1. Too little land might be available for food production

MiniLAB: Try at Home (page 4)
1. Answers will vary; most households discard more paper than anything else.
2. Possible answers: buying materials with less packaging, revising certain items.

Lab (page 5)

Lab Preview
1. to determine if natural materials decompose faster or more slowly than artificial
2. apron, goggles, disposal, sharp objects, handwashing

Conclude and Apply
1. The natural fiber clothing squares should decay more rapidly.
2. Clothing made from natural materials will take up landfill space in short term, but they will decay rapidly, opening up space in the future.
3. Because artificial materials are not biodegradable, they will take up landfill space for a long period of time.
4. Answers will vary based on student's individual research.

Lab: Model and Invent (page 7)

Lab Preview
1. to illustrate population growth over 10 years
2. 1 million new people

Analyze Your Data
1. Students' graphs should show a steady increase in population over the 10 years.
2. Use 6.1 billion for the year 2000 as the starting point. (71,000,000/year × 50 years) + 6,100,000,000 = 9,650,000,000 people in 50 years.
3. (4,500,000/year × 10 years) + 6,100,000,000 = 6,145,000,000

Conclude and Apply
1. 78,000,000/year × 10 years = 780,000,000 in 10 years. Based on 2000 population of 6.1 billion, Earth's population in ten years will be 780,000,000 + 6,100,000,000 = 6,880,000,000 people.
2. Both show population growth. However, population growth is much slower in industrialized nations than in developing countries.
3. Possible answers: People will use more fuel and mineral resources. Land use will increase, resulting in habitat destruction and increased soil erosion. Air and water pollution may increase.

Laboratory Activity 1 (page 9)

Questions and Conclusions
1. prevents infiltration, adds calcium carbonate to adjacent areas, reflects heat and light, adds lead poison to strip along roads, destroys wildlife habitat
2. It adds hydrocarbon gases (carbon monoxide) to the atmosphere, as well as some smoke.
3. bicycling, walking, driving newer cars with anti-pollution equipment, taking public transportation, such as trains or buses
4. Answers will vary. Possibilities include local industries, cars, and burning of dumps.
5. Answers will vary. Possibilities may include scrubbers on smokestacks to remove some gases, electronic air cleaners to remove some particulate matter, or using less fossil fuels.
6. Possibilities include granite, limestone, or sandstone blocks and clay, gravel for concrete or asphalt, wood, petroleum products.
7. farming areas, resources of sand, gravel, clay, recreation areas, wood, wooded/natural areas, nature preserves/wildlife habitats.
8. Alternatives include leaving green areas in cities and zoning certain areas for recreation and/or farming or nature preserves. Students may also think of others.
9. Answers will vary; most drawbacks involve cost.

Laboratory Activity 2 (page 13)

Data and Observations

Table 1

Top row: blue, no change, clear solution
Second row: clear, turns red, copper coating on iron

Questions and Conclusions
1. The copper(II) sulfate dissolves in water and makes available copper ions.
2. The iron provides a means to extract the copper from the solution.
3. A chemical reaction is being used.
4. Sulfuric acid is formed.
5. No; iron and sulfuric acid remain.
6. The stream might become too acidic for fish and water plants to exist. Most copper mines try to find a market for the sulfuric acid.
7. Heavy rain would dissolve the copper (II) sulfate and carry it into streams or into underground water.

Meeting Individual Needs

Directed Reading for Content Mastery (page 17)

Overview (page 17)
1. burns fossil fuels
2. air pollution

3. uses water
4. water pollution
5. uses land
6. soil erosion
7. cuts trees
8. loss of forests
9. creates garbage
10. pollution from landfills
11. population
12. carrying capacity
13. pollutants
14. recycling

Sections 1 and 2 (page 18)

1. People are living longer and having more children. This means the population is growing faster and using more resources.
2. People must use resources carefully so they will have enough for all.
3. Farmers will plow up more land and use herbicides, pesticides, and chemical fertilizers that can damage the topsoil.
4. Land must be used for new houses, streets, and parking lots. New landfills must be built. Trees will be cut down; topsoil will be lost, and rainwater runoff can cause flooding.
5. It is possible that pollution from the landfill could enter the stream.
6. Cars and trucks release pollution from their exhausts.

Section 3 (page 19)

1. c
2. b
3. a
4. b
5. Fewer resources have to be used to make new materials.
6. Fewer resources must be used because fewer packages and other materials are needed.
7. It uses less oil-based fuel, such as gasoline.
8. It provides nutrients for the garden or flower bed, and would reduce the trash input into landfills by 20 percent.
9. More people and trucks are needed to haul materials from the trash. The materials must be separated at special facilities. Items made from recycled materials often cost more.

Key Terms (page 20)

1. sanitary landfills
2. conservation
3. population
4. enzymes
5. stream discharge
6. Composting
7. Recycling
8. Hazardous wastes
9. carrying capacity
10. pollutant

Lectura dirigida para Dominio del contenido (pág. 21)

Sinopsis (pág. 21)

1. quema combustibles fósiles
2. contaminación del aire
3. usa el agua
4. contaminación del agua
5. usa terrenos
6. erosión del suelo
7. tala árboles
8. pérdida de bosques
9. crea basura
10. contaminación de vertederos controlados
11. población
12. capacidad de carga
13. contaminantes
14. reciclaje

Secciones 1 y 2 (pág. 22)

1. La gente vive más tiempo y tiene más hijos. Esto significa que la población está creciendo más rápidamente y usando más recursos.
2. La gente debe usar los recursos sabiamente para que haya suficientes recursos para todos.
3. Los agricultores aran más suelo y usan más herbicidas, pesticidas y fertilizantes químicos que pueden causar daños a la capa de suelo arable.
4. La tierra debe usarse para nuevas viviendas, calles y parqueaderos. Se deben construir nuevos vertederos sanitarios. Se talan los árboles; se pierde la capa de suelo arable y la escorrentía puede causar inundaciones.
5. Es posible que la contaminación del vertedero entre en la corriente de agua.
6. Los vehículos motorizados liberan contaminantes de sus tubos de escape.

Sección 3 (pág. 23)

1. c
2. b
3. a
4. b
5. Se deben usar menos recursos para elaborar nuevos materiales.
6. Se deben usar menos recursos porque se necesitan menos materiales de empaque y otros materiales.
7. Usa menos combustibles del petróleo, como la gasolina.
8. Provee nutrientes para el jardín o huerta y reduciría, en un 20 por ciento, la adición de basura a los vertederos.
9. **Se requieren** más personas y vehículos motorizados para cargar la basura. Los componentes de la basura se deben separar en instalaciones especiales. Los artículos elaborados a partir de materiales reciclados a menudo cuestan más.

Términos claves (pág. 24)

1. vertedero sanitario
2. conservación

3. población
4. enzimas
5. cauce de corriente
6. Hacer abono orgánico
7. Reciclaje
8. Desechos peligrosos
9. capacidad de carga
10. contaminante

Reinforcement (page 25)

Section 1 (page 25)

1. People believed Earth had unlimited resources. Today we know that unless we treat resources carefully, they will be used up.
2. Population is the total number of individuals of a particular species in a particular area.
3. It shows how rapidly the world population doubles.
4. The average lifespan of people who eat nourishing foods has increased.
5. Answers will vary, but should include shortage of food supplies, shortage of energy resources, more pollution, overflowing landfills.
6. electricity use
7. water use
8. farming
9. making products
10. packaging products

Section 2 (page 26)

1. natural
2. people
3. natural
4. people
5. people
6. people
7. natural
8. people
9. people
10. people
11. No. 2—that the landfill was lined to prevent seepage or was located in clay-rich soil.
12. No. 10—composting
13. Nos. 4, 6, possibly 9
14. No. 5—less coal would be needed for generating electricity; No. 8—landfills wouldn't fill as rapidly if recyclable materials weren't put into them.

Section 3 (page 27)

1. an object suitable to be processed and used again
2. Answers should include three of the following: Fewer trees would be cut, landfills would not fill up as quickly, less water is needed to make paper from recycled pulp than from trees, there's less pollution.
3. Twenty aluminum cans can be recycled with the energy needed to make one new can from ore.

4. Consumers are encouraged to recycle the beverage containers to get back the deposit they paid when they bought the beverage.
5. by 60 percent
6. People who recycle pay lower trash-collection fees. Garbage is not collected if it contains recyclable items. Refundable deposits are made on all beverage containers.
7. Answers will vary. Students may say they could use both sides of notebook paper, cut old clothes into cleaning rags, use rags in place of paper towels, reuse plastic and paper bags, and compost yard waste.
8. Some students may say recycling is very important and if consumers will not recycle without laws, then they should be made, by law, to recycle. Others may say there are more important issues for lawmakers and police to concentrate on, so recycling should be voluntary.

Enrichment (page 28)

Section 1 (page 28)

1. 6.05 billion
2. Students will answer either yes or no; 60.5 million
3. 2% = 121 million
4. It falls between them
5. The number of births would have to equal the number of deaths.
6. The population would remain at 6.05 billion because if births and deaths equal each other, the population would stay the same as it was in 2000.
7. Answers will vary. Some students may say that the information could help the U.N. plan for areas where people will need more food, medicine, or housing.

Section 2 (page 29)

1. The area is high in the mountains, where the air is thin and holds less heat.
2. Subjects that could be covered include the following: world hunger; contamination by herbicides and pesticides; efficient use of land area; using land rather than paving it; and composting and using organic waste.

Section 3 (page 30)

1. recyclable cardboard cartons or reusable suitcases, trunks, boxes, etc.
2. old toys, old clothes
3. metal, plastic (including records), school papers
4. medicines, science experiments (perhaps), makeup
5. dead plants, science experiments (perhaps)

Note-Taking Worksheet (page 31)

Refer to teacher outline, student answers are underlined.

Assessment

Chapter Review (page 35)

Part A. Vocabulary Review (page 35)
1. population (1/1)
2. sanitary landfill (5/2)
3. carrying capacity (1/1)
4. composting (7/3)
5. recycling (7/3)
6. hazardous waste (5/2)
7. conservation (7/3)
8. Enzymes (5/2)
9. pollutant (3/1)
10. stream discharge (5/2)
11. carbon dioxide(5/2)
12. Radioactive (5/2)

Part B. Concept Review (page 36)
1. More people are living longer and remaining in the population. (2/1)
2. clean water, better nutrition (2/1)
3. Plastic is refined from oil. The process of refining oil produces pollutants. Plastic also takes up landfill space. (3/1)
4. The average person living in the U.S. uses several times as much energy as the average person in the rest of the world. (3/1)
5. Herbicides and pesticides make their way to waterways where they contaminate the environment. Such pollutants may cause cancer. Tilling cropland causes topsoil erosion. (5/2)
6. a square kilometer of vegetable crops (4/2)
7. Species lose their habitats. Reduced vegetation can result in higher levels of carbon dioxide in the atmosphere. Some species may become extinct. Less water enters the atmosphere meaning less rainfall in local areas. (5/2)
8. It prevents water from soaking into the soil. (5/2)
9. Recycling reduces trash generated in a person's lifetime by 60 percent. It saves energy, natural resources, and landfill space. (8/3)

Chapter Test (page 37)

I. Testing Concepts (page 37)
1. false, 200,000 (1/1)
2. false, paving over land prevents water from soaking into soil (5/2)
3. true (8/3)
4. true (6/2)
5. true (5/2)
6. false, a container law requires a refundable deposit on most beverage containers (7/3)
7. false, although sanitary landfills are lined, some hazardous substances may still leak into the soil (5/2)
8. true (3/1)
9. true (7/3)

10. false, the term composting means piling up grass clippings and leaves so they can decompose (7/3)
11. d (1/1)
12. b (7/3)
13. a (8/3)
14. c (2/1)
15. a (5/2)
16. d (5/2)
17. c (4/2)
18. c (8/3)
19. d (5/2)
20. b (5/2)

II. **Understanding Concepts (page 39)**
1. **I. A.** 1 or 4
2.   **B.** 1 or 4
3. **II. A.** 5 or 6
4.   **B.** 5 or 6
5. **III. A.** 3 or 2
6.   **B.** 3 or 2
7. 3.0 billion (1/1)
8. 150 years (1/1)
9. 400 million (1/1)
10. about 500,000 years ago (1/1)

III. **Applying Concepts (page 40)**
1. An American consumer uses electricity that is usually generated by burning fossil fuels, uses water that needs cleaning, and eats foods that take the land, pesticides, and herbicides to grow. He or she buys overpackaged materials that generate waste. (3/1)
2. It would save 26 million trees; keeping 26 million trees alive would save habitats. (8/3)
3. Covering the garbage with soil prevents it from blowing away and reduces odor. Linings reduce the chance that pollutants will leak into the soil and underground water. (6/2)
4. Citizens can practice conservation by reducing their use of materials, reusing and recycling materials and composting. (7/3)
5. Answers will vary. If effective recycling is occurring without legislation, most people would agree that it can continue that way. Those who think recycling is needed will want government action if other means have not been effective. (8/3)

Section Focus Transparency 1 (page 42)

All Tied Up

Transparency Teaching Tips
- This transparency introduces population impact and carrying capacity. Ask the students to discuss the sources of the traffic jam as shown on the transparency.
- Explain the concept of carrying capacity (largest number of individuals of a species a specific environment will support). Ask the students to consider the impact population is having on the roads in their community and to relate this impact to the broader concept of carrying capacity.
- Point out that the world's population will almost double in the next 100 years. Discuss how this will impact the students' lives.
- Discuss the effects of increased population on the environment.

Content Background
- World population reached one billion in the 1820s. In the intervening 180 years, the population has increased six times over, to more than six billion. As previously stated, it is estimated that world population will double to 12 billion in the next 100 years.
- For the next years a record number of children will attend school in the United States—over 70 million in total (28 percent of the population).

Answers to Student Worksheet
1. Yes it has. The road is full.
2. Answers will vary. While more roads may alleviate the current problems, they will eventually fill up, too.
3. Alternative ways of travel could solve the problem. Different forms of mass public transportation might lessen traffic.

Section Focus Transparency 2 (page 43)

Land and Water

Transparency Teaching Tips
- The focus here is land usage and its effect on the environment. Ask the students what the first photo has to do with the second. Point out that natural wetlands act as catch basins for water run-off. Ask the students what would happen if a wetland were filled in with dirt and covered with concrete. (Flooding might result.)
- Explain that the major types of wetlands (swamps, marshes, bogs, and fens) are differentiated by the types of the types of flora in each).

Content Background
- Wetlands are among Earth's most productive and important ecosystems. They function as a transition zone between land and water systems.
- Wetlands prevent flooding, clean polluted water, and protect shoreline.
- In the United States, between 70,000 and 90,000 acres of wetlands are being lost annually, despite increased awareness and governmental efforts to preserve them.
- Over a million acres of wetlands have been lost in the United States in the last 400 years, approximately half of the total wetland acreage.
- Wetlands are damaged through draining, dredging, construction, mining, tilling, and the building of levees, among others.

Answers to Student Worksheet
1. Wetlands can protect other areas from flooding by absorbing water.
2. Answers will vary. One possible answer is to avoid developing wetland areas.

Section Focus Transparency 3 (page 44)

Relaxin' On The Refuse

Transparency Teaching Tips
- The concept here is recycling. Ask the students how many of their families recycle. Ask them to explain the reasoning behind recycling.
- Explain that recycling saves raw materials, reduces pollution, and reduces waste sent to landfills.

Content Background
- Recycling is usually defined as the saving, recovering, and reprocessing of discarded materials for use in new products.
- There are 5,000 to 10,000 recycling companies in the United States.
- The United States produces more than 200 million tons of refuse annually. We recycle approximately 25 percent of that total.
- Recycling one ton of newsprint saves approximately 17 trees.

Answers to Student Worksheet
1. Reusing materials saves raw materials, reduces pollution, and reduces landfill usage.
2. Answers will vary. Paper, plastics, metals, tires, cans, batteries, and glass are among the possible answers.

Teaching Transparency (Page 45)

Destruction of the Rain Forest

Section 2

Transparency Teaching Tips
- Point out to students that everything on Earth is connected. When something happens to the air, water, or soil, it affects plants and animals, too. When something happens to plants and animals, the air, water, and soil may also be affected.

Reteaching Suggestion
- Many human activities indirectly affect the air, water, and soil. Humans increase the amount of carbon dioxide in the air by burning fossil fuels and by cutting down forests. Humans affect soil and land by polluting it, and by clearing the land for building.

Extensions
Research: Have the students choose a positive way humans can affect the air, water, or soil. Write a paper explaining what activity canbe done to help the area chosen.

Challenge: In small groups have students come up with a plan to help the environment that can be done at school.

Answers to Student Worksheet
1. Answers may vary but may include the idea that it may cause the extinction of many plants and animals.
2. reforestation
3. 28%
4. carbon dioxide
5. Answers may vary but could include the increase of the Earth's surface temperature.

Assessment Transparency (Page 47)

Our Impact on Land

Section 3

Answers
1. C. To answer this question, the student must read *carefully*. The chart indicates the amount of water used to wash dirty dishes and to wash dirty clothes.
2. G. This question requires students to use the information in the chart to make a conclusion. In order to identify the correct answer choice, students must look at the information in the *Number of Times Activity Done Per Day* column.

Test-Taking Tip
Remind students to always *read the question carefully* to determine exactly what information they are being asked to find.